Anne Geddes

MY FIRST FIVE YEARS

2000

- MY BIRTH -

My name is

I was born on

at

The time was

I was delivered by

I weighed

and measured

My eyes were

My hair was

- MEMENTOS -

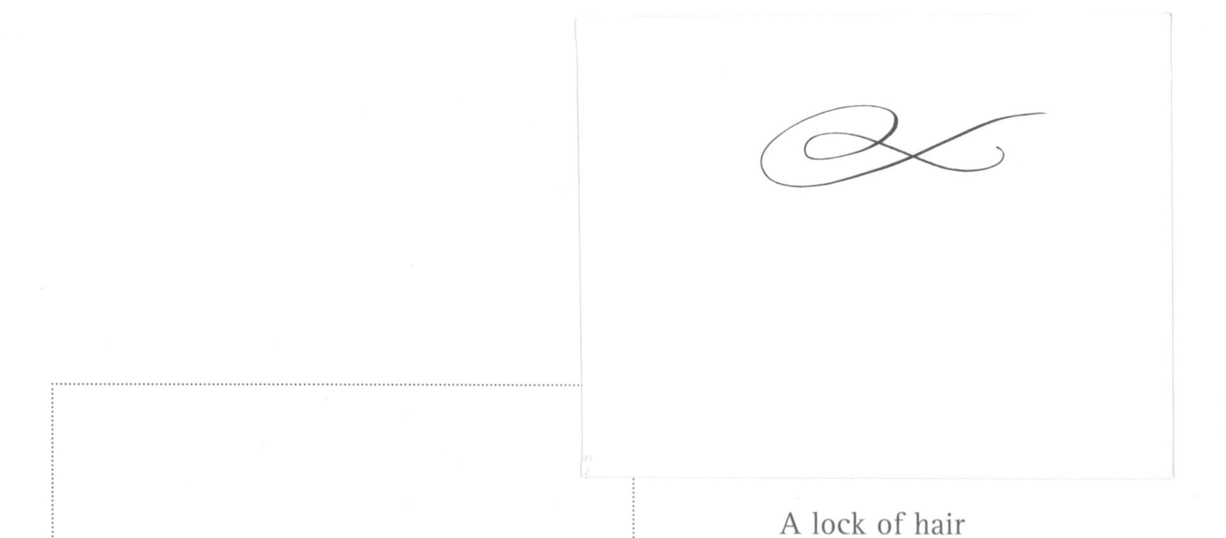

My hospital tag

A lock of hair

My Birth Announcement

- NEWSPAPER CLIPPINGS -

- PHOTOGRAPHS -

EUROPA
AFRICA

- SPECIAL MESSAGES -

Mother

Father

Family

Friends

- VISITORS AND GIFTS -

- SIGNS -

Star Sign

Chinese Year

Birthstone

Birth Flower

Birth Day Horoscope

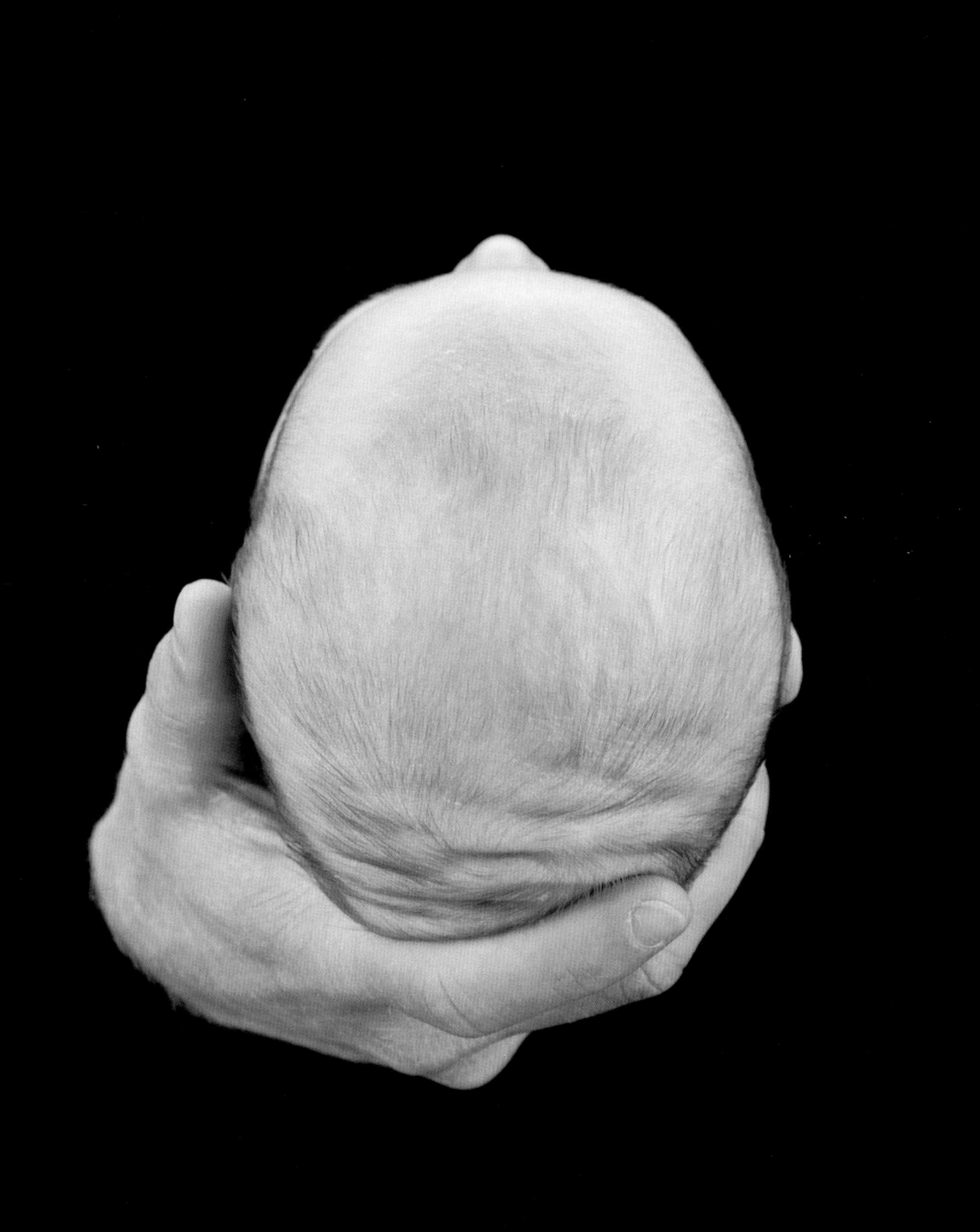

My full name is

My names were chosen by

because

My pet names are

I was christened on

at

Comments

- MY FAMILY TREE -

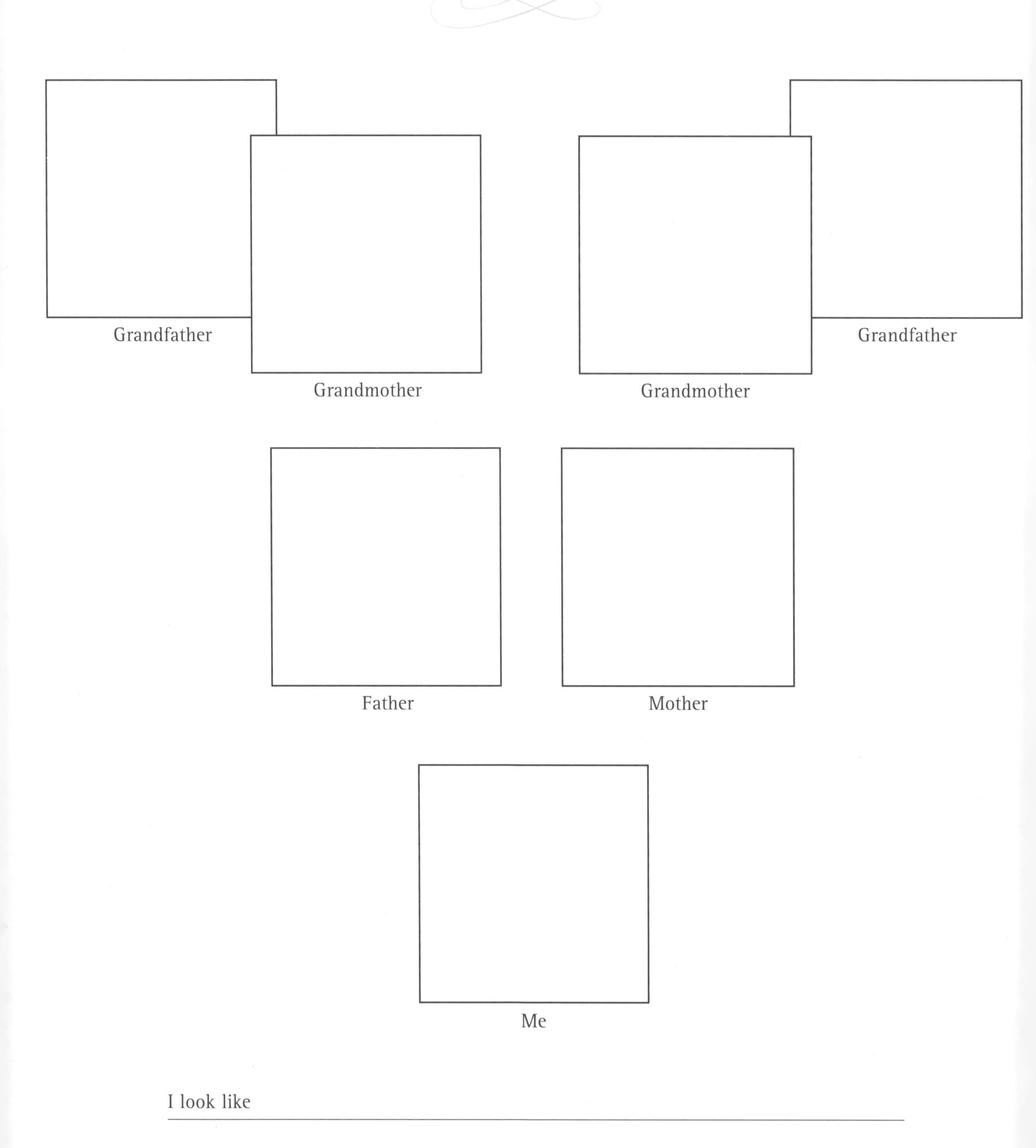

I look like ______________________________

- PHOTOGRAPHS -

- THREE MONTHS -

Weight

Length

Comments

- PHOTOGRAPHS -

- SIX MONTHS -

Weight

Length

Comments

- PHOTOGRAPHS -

- NINE MONTHS -

Weight

Length

Comments

- MY FIRST BIRTHDAY -

I live at

My height is

Weight

Sayings

Toys

Pets

Books

- PHOTOGRAPHS -

- MY PARTY -

Date

Where held

Friends and relations there

My presents

- MILESTONES -

I first smiled

laughed

grasped a toy

I slept through the night

I held my head up

rolled over

sat up

I first crawled

stood up

walked

My first tooth

My first word

Other milestones

SALTER
TRADE
SPRING BALANCE
Nº 501
VENDORS ONLY

- PHOTOGRAPHS -

- FOOD -

My first solid food

I was weaned

I drank from a cup

I fed myself

Finger food

I like

I don't like

- MY FIRST CHRISTMAS -

It was at

Other people there

My presents

- MY FIRST HOLIDAY -

It was at

Date

The weather was

Other people there

What we did

Comments

- CLOTHES -

The first time I dressed myself

I wore

My favourite dress-ups

I won't wear

Comments

- FAVOURITES -

Music

Rhymes

Clothes

Animals

Activities

Television programmes

I really don't like

- BEST FRIENDS -

Comments

One Year

Two Years

Three Years

Four Years

Comments

Five Years

- MY SECOND BIRTHDAY -

I live at

My height is

Weight

Sayings

Toys

Pets

Books

- PHOTOGRAPHS -

- MY PARTY -

Date

Where held

Friends and relations there

My presents

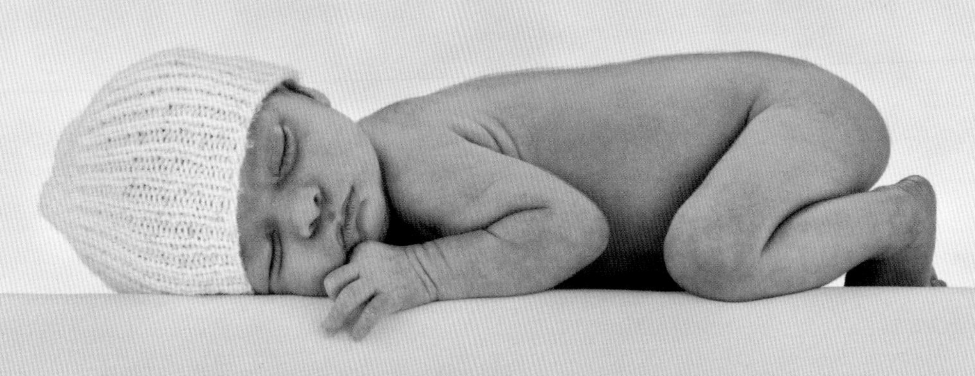
1 INCHES 2 3 4 5 6 7 8 9 10 11 12
1 2 3 CMS 4 5 6 7 8 9 10 11 12 13 14 15 16 17 18 19 20 21 22 23 24 25 26 27 28 29 30

- MY THIRD BIRTHDAY -

I live at

My height is

Weight

Sayings

Toys

Pets

Books

- PHOTOGRAPHS -

- MY PARTY -

Date

Where held

Friends and relations there

My presents

- PRESCHOOL -

I started on

My preschool is called

My friends there are

What I like to do there

- MY FOURTH BIRTHDAY -

I live at

My height is

Weight

Sayings

Toys

Pets

Books

- PHOTOGRAPHS -

- MY PARTY -

Date

Where held

Friends and relations there

My presents

- MY FIFTH BIRTHDAY -

I live at

My height is

Weight

Sayings

Toys

Pets

Books

- PHOTOGRAPHS -

- MY PARTY -

Date

Where held

Friends and relations there

My presents

- SCHOOL -

My first day at school was on

The school is called

My teacher is

What I did on the first day

My friends are

Comments

- DRAWINGS -

- WRITING -

I could recite the alphabet

I started to write

I began to read

My writing

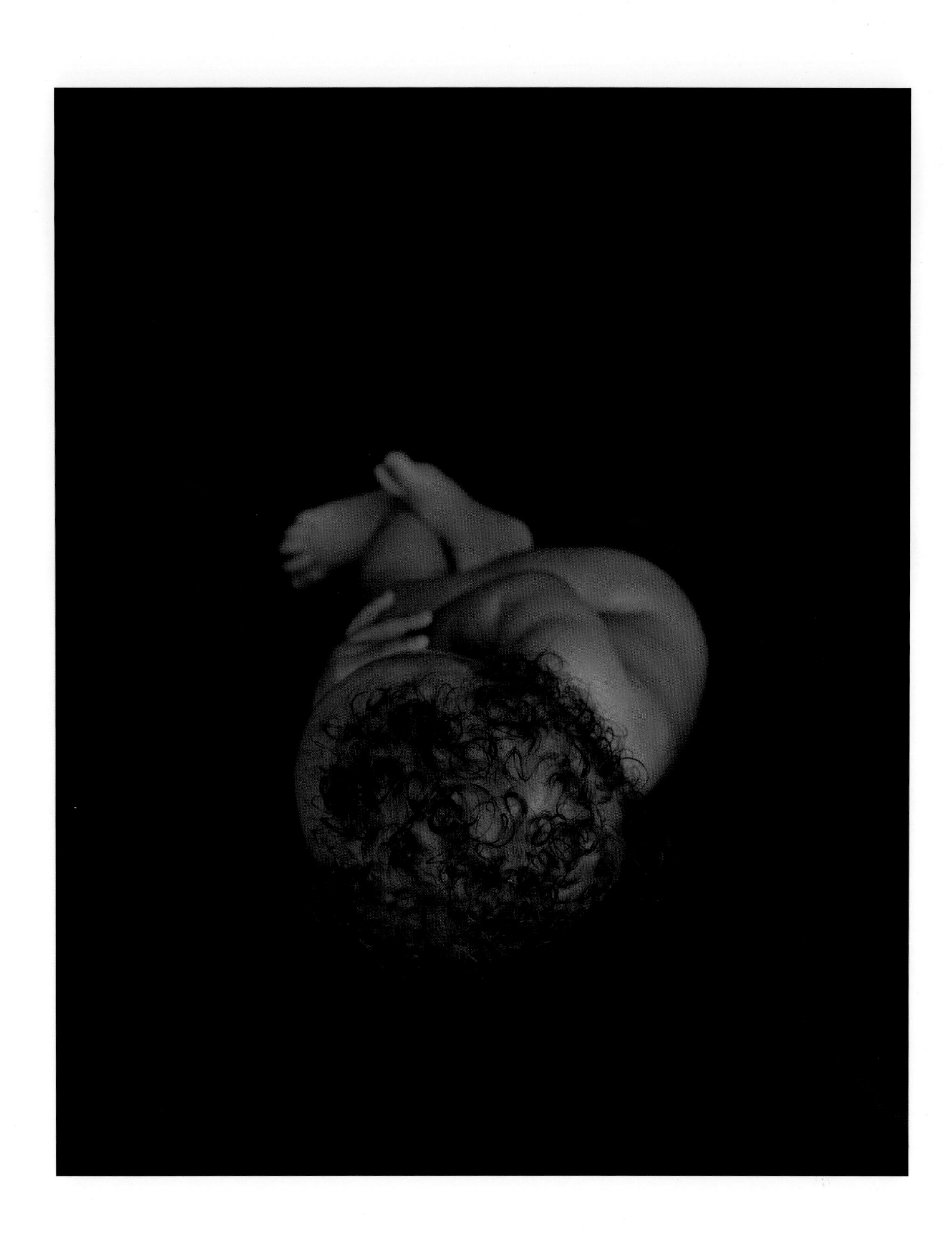

- HEALTH -

IMMUNISATION

Age	Vaccine	Date given

Illnesses

Allergies

Comments

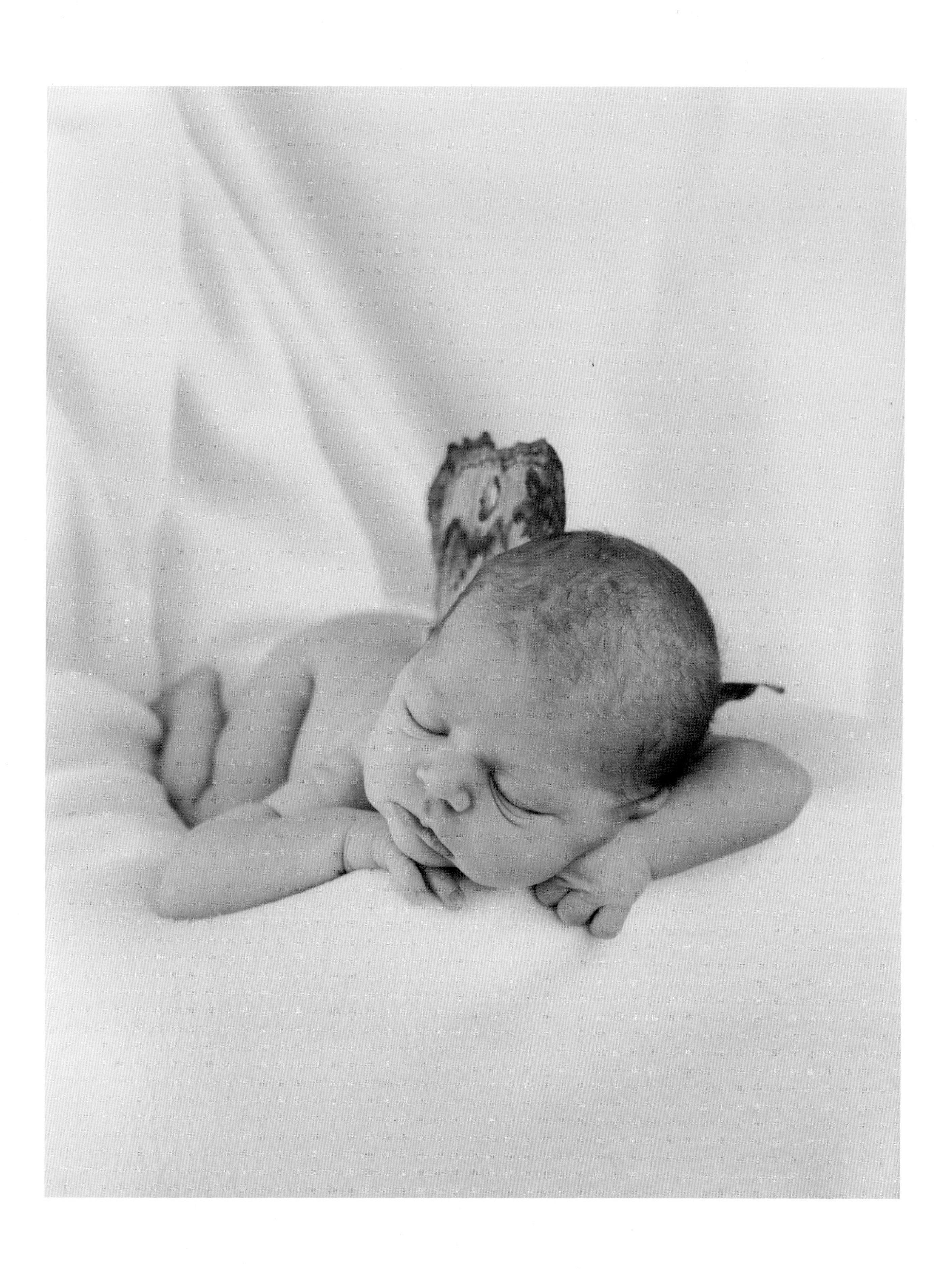

- MY HEIGHT -

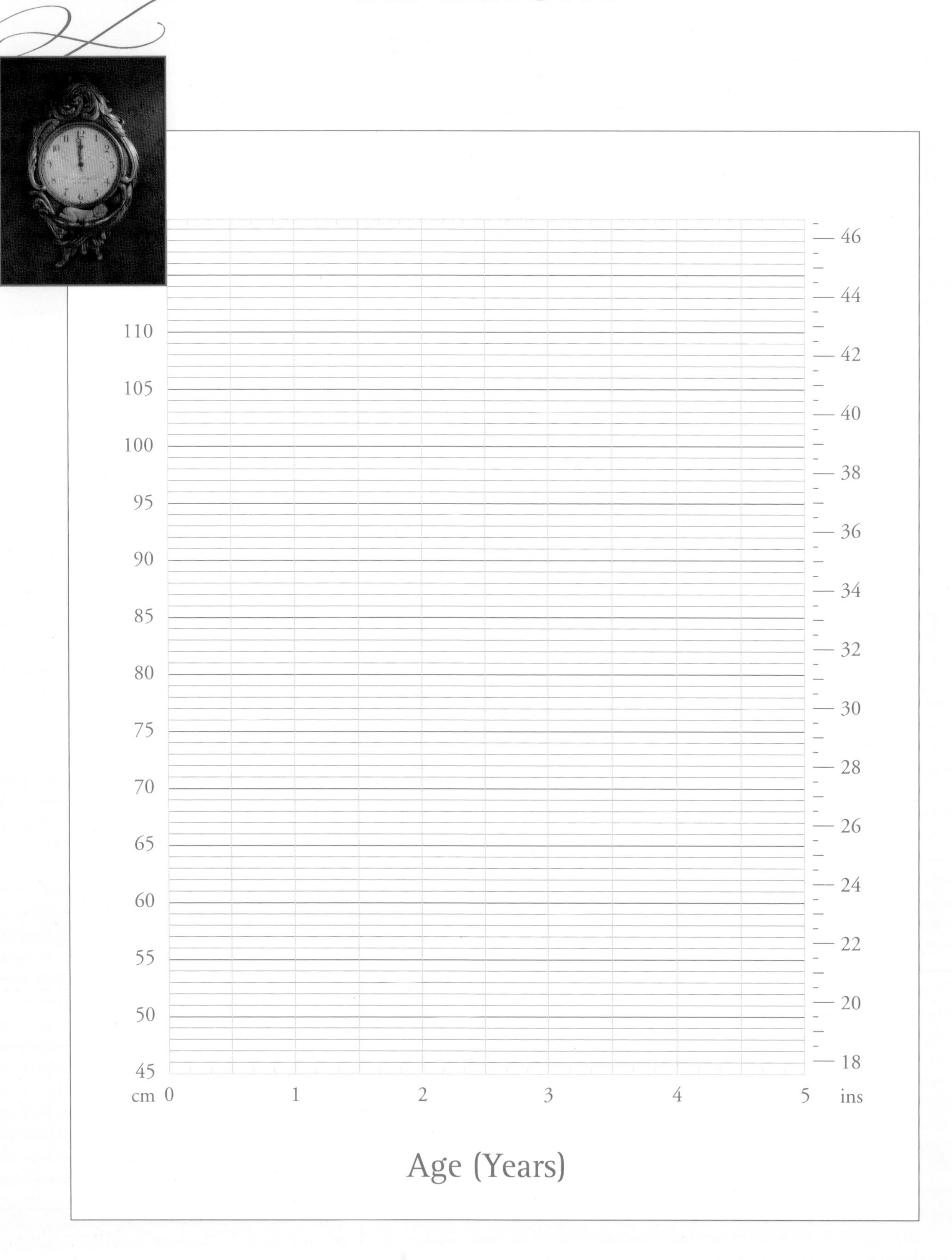

110
105
100
95
90
85
80
75
70
65
60
55
50
45
cm
0
1
2
3
4
5
46
44
42
40
38
36
34
32
30
28
26
24
22
20
18
ins
Age (Years)

- MY WEIGHT -

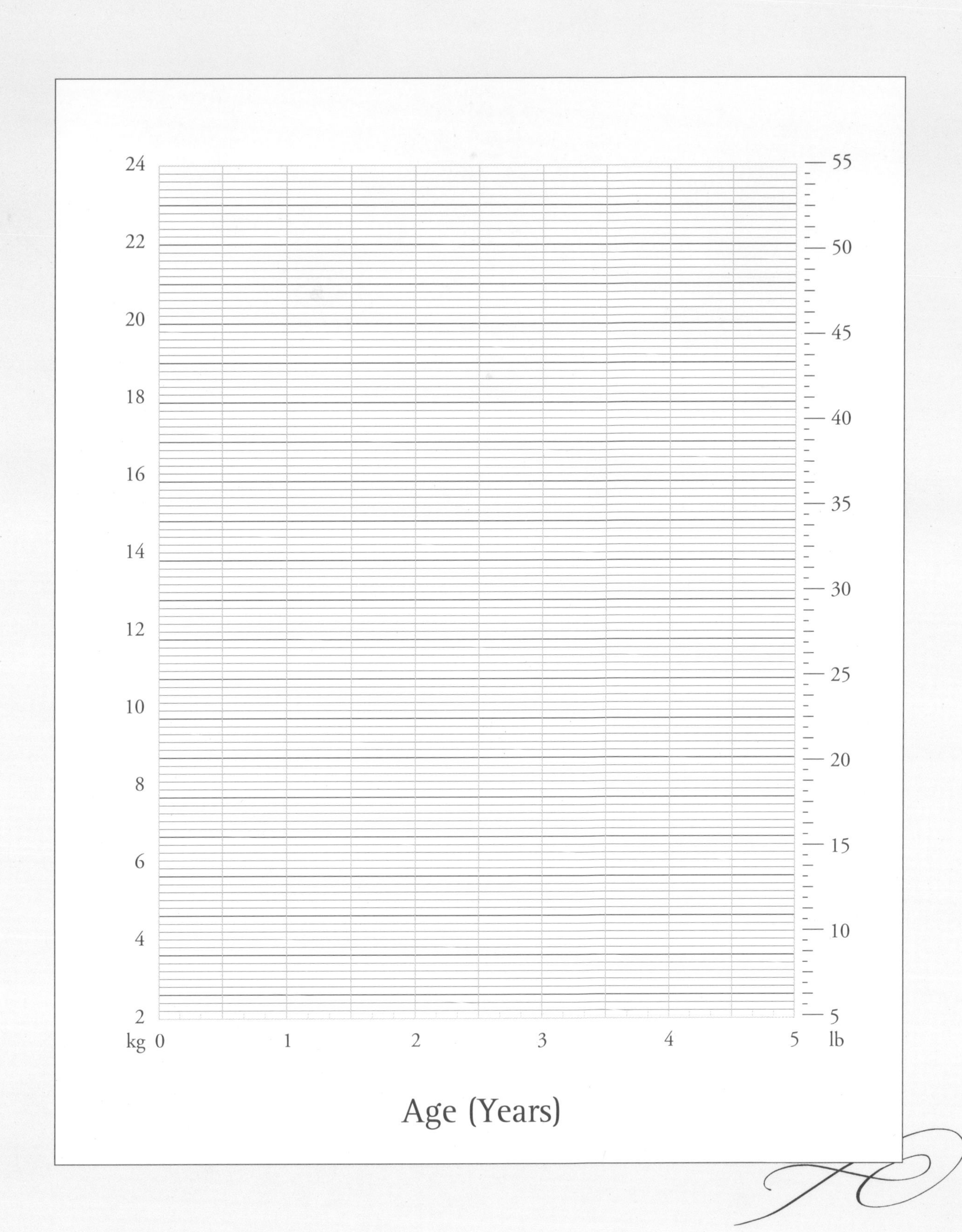
24
22
20
18
16
14
12
10
8
6
4
2
kg
0
1
2
3
4
5
55
50
45
40
35
30
25
20
15
10
5
lb
Age (Years)

- TOOTH FAIRY'S PAGE -

I lost my first tooth on

The Tooth Fairy left me

I lost my second tooth on

The Tooth Fairy left me

- MY TEETH -

Upper Jaw Dates

8

9

16

13

24

Months

24

13

16

10

7

Lower Jaw Dates

Dental Nurse Visits

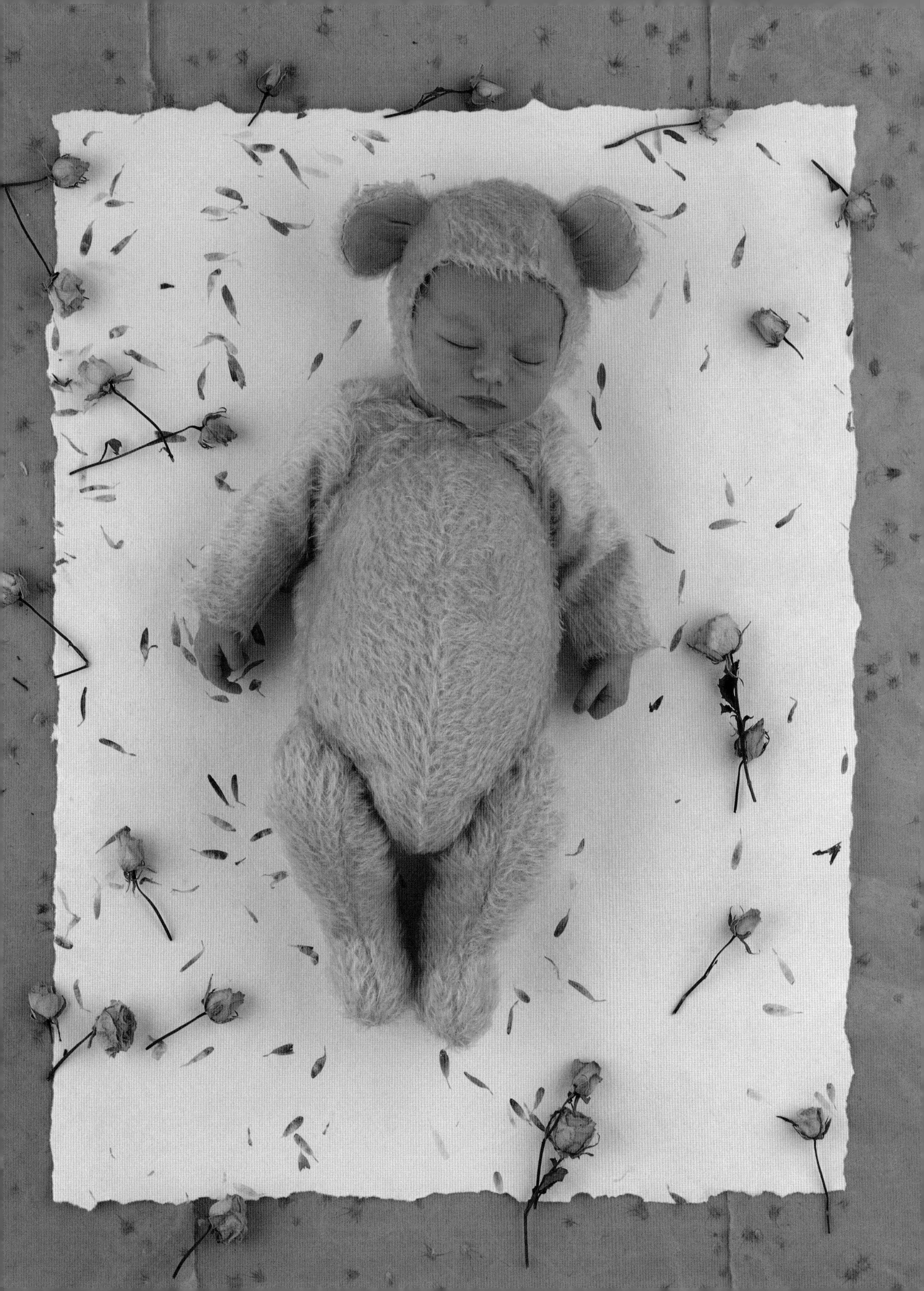

- MY HANDPRINTS -

At birth

At five years

- MY FOOTPRINTS -

At birth

At five years

- BIRTHSTONES -

JANUARY	Garnet – constancy, truth
FEBRUARY	Amethyst – sincerity, humility
MARCH	Aquamarine – courage, energy
APRIL	Diamond – innocence, success
MAY	Emerald – tranquillity
JUNE	Pearl – preciousness, purity
JULY	Ruby – freedom from care, chastity
AUGUST	Moonstone – joy
SEPTEMBER	Sapphire – hope, chastity
OCTOBER	Opal – reflecting every mood
NOVEMBER	Topaz – fidelity, loyalty
DECEMBER	Turquoise – love, success

- FLOWERS -

JANUARY	Snowdrop – pure and gentle
FEBRUARY	Carnation – bold and brave
MARCH	Violet – modest
APRIL	Lily – virtuous
MAY	Hawthorn – bright and hopeful
JUNE	Rose – beautiful
JULY	Daisy – wide-eyed and innocent
AUGUST	Poppy – peaceful
SEPTEMBER	Morning Glory – easily contented
OCTOBER	Cosmos – ambitious
NOVEMBER	Chrysanthemum – cheeky and cheerful
DECEMBER	Holly – full of foresight

- STAR SIGNS -

CAPRICORN
22 December – 20 January
Resourceful, self-sufficient,
responsible

AQUARIUS
21 January – 18 February
Great caring for others, very emotional
under cool exterior

PISCES
19 February – 19 March
Imaginative, sympathetic,
tolerant

ARIES
20 March – 20 April
Brave, courageous, energetic, loyal

TAURUS
21 April – 21 May
Sensible,
loves peace and stability

GEMINI
22 May – 21 June
Unpredictable, lively,
charming, witty

CANCER
22 June – 22 July
Loves security and comfort

LEO
23 July – 23 August
Idealistic, romantic,
honourable, loyal

VIRGO
24 August – 23 September
Shy, sensitive,
values knowledge

LIBRA
24 September – 23 October
Diplomatic,
full of charm and style

SCORPIO
24 October – 22 November
Compassionate,
proud, determined

SAGITTARIUS
23 November – 21 December
Bold, impulsive,
seeks adventure

ANNE GEDDES™

www.annegeddes.com

This edition published in 1999 by Photogenique Publishers
(a division of Hodder Moa Beckett)
Studio 3.16, Axis Building, 1 Cleveland Road, Parnell
Auckland, New Zealand

First published in Great Britain in 1999
by HEADLINE BOOK PUBLISHING
A division of Hodder Headline PLC
338 Euston Road
London NW1 3BH

10 9 8 7 6 5 4 3 2 1

Produced by Kel Geddes
Colour separations by Image Centre

Printed by Midas Printing Limited, Hong Kong

British Library Cataloguing in Publication Data
for this title is available on request.

ISBN 0 7472 7388 X